Three Piano Preludes

in Jazz Stylings

by Arletta O'Hearn

Commissioned by the Oregon Music Teachers Association

About the composer

Arletta O'Hearn is an independent piano teacher in Portland, Oregon, teaching both jazz and classical repertoire. She also performs as a soloist and with jazz ensembles. She is an active member of the Portland chapter of the Oregon Music Teachers Association, through which she is state certified.

Mrs. O'Hearn has received the Award of Merit from the National Federation of Music Clubs for American Music and was chosen 1984 "Composer of the Year" by the Oregon Music Teachers Association.

Piano Music by Arletta O'Hearn

Jazz Theme and Variations (two pianos) WP89
Jazz Together (one piano, four hands) WP120

Love Jazz WP80
Sunshine and Blues WP84
Three Piano Preludes WP141

ISBN 0-8497-5255-8

Prelude
I

Arletta O'Hearn

© 1984 Kjos West

Prelude
II

Arletta O'Hearn

Prelude
III

Arletta O'Hearn

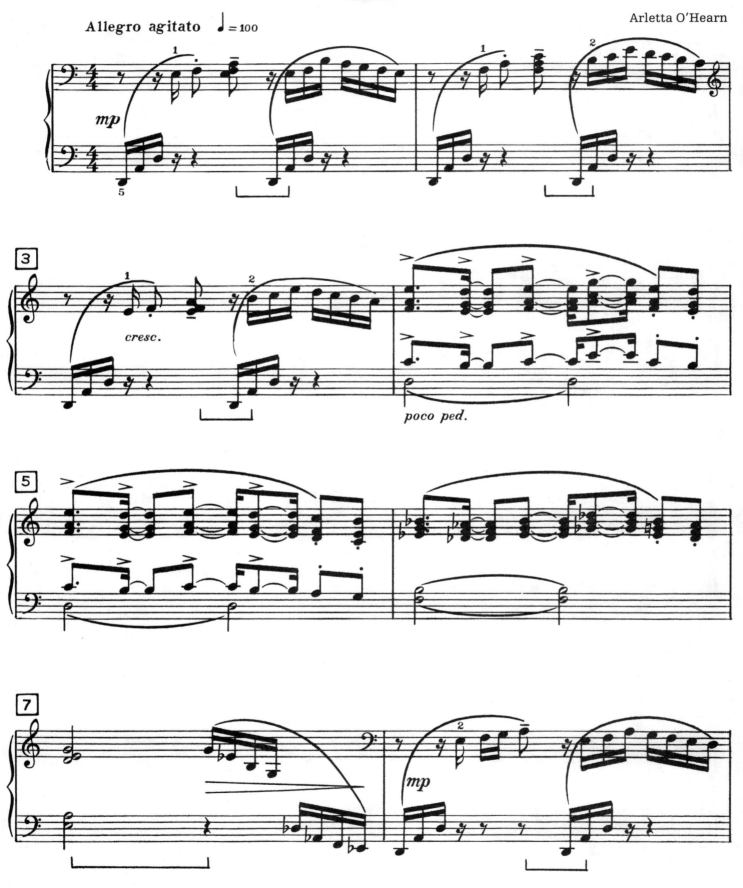

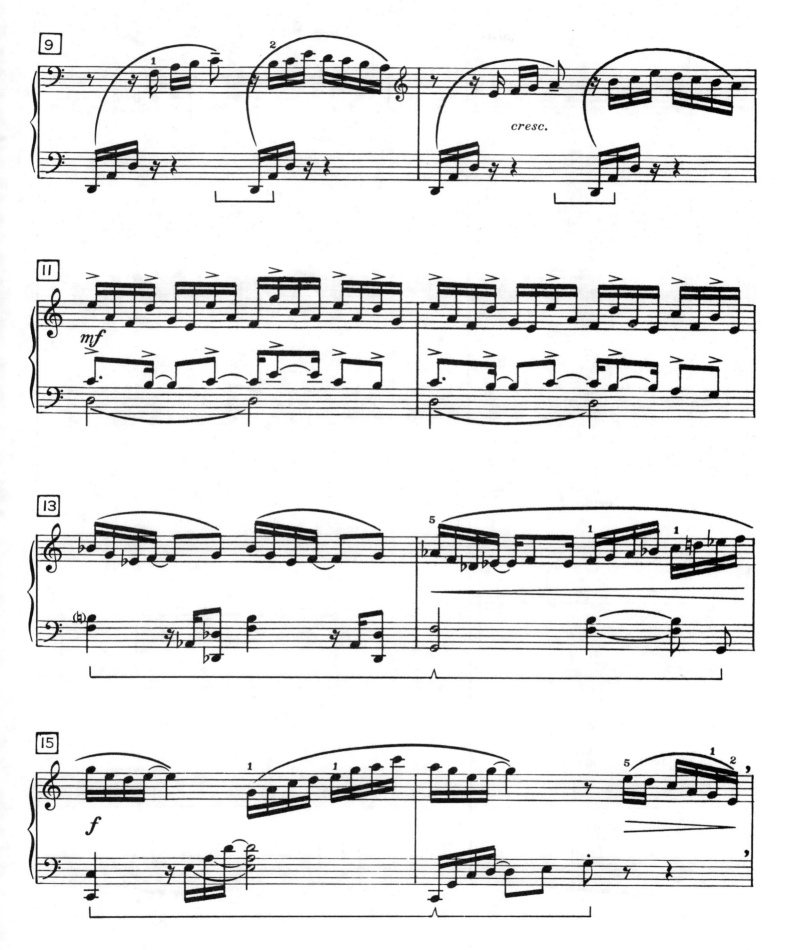